Let's Talk About

BEING RUDE

Let's Talk About

BEING RUDE

By JOY BERRY

Illustrated by John Costanza
Edited by Orly Kelly
Designed by Jill Losson

GROLIER ENTERPRISES CORP.

Let's talk about BEING RUDE.

When you treat other people as though they are not as important as you are, you are BEING RUDE.

You are being rude when you insist on being *first*.

When you insist on always having the *best* for yourself, you are being rude.

You are being rude when you insist on having the *most* for yourself.

When you insist on always being the *center of attention* by having everyone notice you and no one else, you are being rude.

You are being rude when you insist on
always *having your own way.*

People who are being rude are being selfish and unkind.

No one likes to be around a person who is rude.

If you do not want to be rude, do not insist on being *first*.

Do not get in front of people or try to push them out of the way so that you can be first.

Patiently wait for your turn.

Do not insist on always having the *best* for yourself if you do not want to be rude.

If you do not want to be rude, do not insist on having the *most* for yourself.

Do not insist on always being the *center of attention* if you do not want to be rude. It is OK to have people pay attention to you. But everyone should not have to pay attention to you and no one else all of the time.

If you do not want to be rude, do not insist on always having your way. Things should not always have to happen the way you want them to happen.

If you do not want to be rude —

- do not say or do anything that would hurt another person;
- do not do anything that would damage or destroy another person's things;
- listen when people are talking and do not speak until they are finished talking;
- be as quiet as you can around people who are sleeping, resting, talking with others, thinking, watching TV, or listening to something.

It is important that you treat other people the way you want to be treated.

If you do not want people to be rude to you, you must not be rude to them.